WHAT THEY DON'T SEE

A LITTLE GIRL'S MOMENT OF HONESTY

Written by
Ashley M. Paul

Illustrated and Designed by
Fx And Color Studio

Dedication

To the children whose tears go unnoticed.

Mom. Dad.
You are both really great!

But there's this one thing I've been afraid to say...
I'm happier when you're apart.

Mom, you have a heart of gold and have a smile that lights up the city! But, what you don't see is...

You seem happier
when you're apart.

Dad, you fight crime and have always been **our hero.**

Your laugh is magnetic and just to hear it
can draw anyone in...
But you, also,
seem happier when you're apart.

You see, the things that are wonderful about you both haven't made you so **wonderful** for each other for quite some time and...

I'm happier when you're apart.
Your smiles and laughter have turned into
a cold silence and awkward stares...

Why can't you see it?
What would it mean for you two
to truly be apart?

What you don't see is me.

Yes, me!

and me, crying myself to sleep at night.
I'm so much happier when you're apart.

Trying to "keep the peace"
hasn't been so peaceful.

Yeah, I see how hard you've tried.
But Mom.
Dad.
Sometimes I just wish you could
see that this hasn't been healthy for me.
This is my moment of honesty.

For Parents to ask:

How do you feel when you see or hear mommy and daddy arguing?

Do you think it is your fault?

What do you do when we are arguing?

Do you think we are going to hurt each other when we disagree about something?

Do you feel safe when we argue?

Ask Yourself:

In what ways can you change your communication style in the presence of your child?

Do you have a specified time every week to address issues with your family? If not, what is a good day and time to establish this family meeting?

For Children to ask:

Why do my parents (you) argue all the time?

Are you arguing about me?

Do you like each other?

Why do you say mean things to each other?

Are you going to leave each other?

If you do leave each other what will
happen to me?

Ask yourself:

What coping skills do you use when you hear your parents arguing?

Do you think this is the best way for parents to communicate?
Why or Why not?

Compare how you communicate with others when you are angry to how
your parents communicate with each other when they are angry.

For Counselors, Teachers, etc:

Have you ever witnessed adults in your home arguing?

Disagreements are a natural part of life. What are some unhealthy ways to disagree with someone?

Is there ever a time when someone should be physical during an argument?

A letter from the Author.

Thank you for reading my book!

Whether it was purchased by you, given as a gift, or stumbled across I am thankful. This book was written with millions of children in mind as well as the little girl within me who finally found healing as an adult. I hope this book brings awareness, healing within the home, and creates opportunity for open and effective communication. Let us remember our little people and remember that they see, hear, and feel more than you know. There are no perfect parents, but the best ones are the ones that listen!

Sincerely,
Ashley M. Paul